HOW TO WRITE AN ESSAY
Writing Skills Series

• •

Written by Brenda Vance Rollins, Ed. D.

GRADES 5 - 8
Reading Levels 3 - 4

Classroom Complete Press
P.O. Box 19729
San Diego, CA 92159
Tel: 1-800-663-3609 | Fax: 1-800-663-3608
Email: service@classroomcompletepress.com

www.classroomcompletepress.com

ISBN-13: 978-1-55319-394-4

ISBN – 10: 1-55319-394-6

© 2009

Permission to Reproduce

Critical Thinking Skills

● ● ● ● ● ● ● ● ● ● ● ● ● ● ● ● ● ●

How to Write an Essay

Skills For Critical Thinking	Chapters											
	1	2	3	4	5	6	7	8	9	10	11	12
LEVEL 1 Remembering • Define, Describe, Identify, Label, List, Match, Name, State	✓	✓	✓	✓	✓	✓	✓	✓	✓	✓	✓	✓
LEVEL 2 Understanding • Describe, Discuss, Explain, Paraphrase, Restate, Summarize	✓	✓	✓	✓	✓	✓	✓	✓	✓	✓	✓	✓
LEVEL 3 Applying • Predict, Project, Provide, Relate, Report; Show		✓	✓		✓		✓		✓		✓	✓
LEVEL 4 Analysing • Illustrate, Infer, Outline, Point Out, Prioritize, Recognize		✓	✓	✓		✓		✓		✓		✓
LEVEL 5 Evaluating • Appraise, Compare and Contrast, Conclude, Decide, Support					✓		✓			✓	✓	✓
LEVEL 6 Creating • Categorize, Compare, Compose, Contrast, Create; Design; Revise	✓	✓	✓	✓	✓	✓	✓	✓	✓	✓	✓	

Based on Bloom's Taxonomy

Contents

✔ **6 BONUS Activity Pages!** Additional worksheets for your students

FREE!

- Go to our website: www.classroomcompletepress.com/**bonus**
- Enter item CC1102
- Enter pass code CC1102D

Assessment Rubric

How to Write an Essay

Student's Name: _____   Assignment: _____   Level: _____

	Level 1	Level 2	Level 3	Level 4
Ideas	• Main idea is unclear. • Little or no topic development. • Little or no detail.	• Main idea may be unclear at times. • The topic is beginning to be developed. • Level of detail is inconsistent	• Main idea of the story is clear through majority of the paper. • Topic has a clear beginning, middle, and end. • Level of detail is sustained through majority of paper.	• Main idea of the story is clear throughout the paper. • The topic is fully elaborated with rich details. • Level of detail is sustained throughout paper.
Organization	• Minimal response to topic; uncertain focus. • Inappropriate or illogical progression of ideas. • No planning evident; disorganized. • Few, if any, transitions between ideas.	• Attempts to focus. • Some lapses or flaws in organization • May lack transitions between ideas	• Sustained focus. • Logical progression of idea. • Moderately fluent. • Transition evident.	• Sustained focus. • Appropriate and logical progression of ideas. • Related ideas are grouped in a logical manner within paragraphs • Varied transitional elements
Style	• Assortment of incomplete and/or incorrect sentences. • Fails to include the writer's imagination and personal experiences that are related to the story. • Narrative elements are missing from the story. • Does not attempt to incorporate narrative strategies. • Writing voice is not noticeable • Details random, inappropriate, or barely apparent.	• Little variety in sentence beginnings, structures, and lengths. • Occasionally includes the writer's imagination and personal experiences that are related to the story • Narrative elements are not consistent throughout the story • Few successful attempts to incorporate narrative strategies • Writing voice is bland and does not engage the reader • Uneven development of details; Details lack elaboration	• Attempts to vary sentence beginnings, structures, and lengths. • Sometimes includes writer's imagination and personal experiences that are related to the story • Contains narrative elements, but some may not be consistent throughout the story. • Some successful attempts to incorporate narrative strategies • Writing voice is bland or at times, fails to engage the reader • Details are appropriate and varied	• Effective variety of sentence beginnings, structures, and lengths. • Includes the writer's imagination and personal experiences that are related to the story. • Contains narrative elements such as characters, plot, point of view, setting, conflict, and significant events. • Successfully incorporates narrative strategies such as flashback, foreshadowing, dialogue, tension, and/or suspense. • Uses a lively writing voice to engage the reader. • Uses vivid, sensory details and concrete language.
Conventions	• Errors prevent the reader from understanding the writer's message.	• Errors interrupt the flow of communication and may interfere with meaning. • Errors do not reflect grade-level expectations in punctuation, grammar, and spelling.	• Some errors are present, but they do not interfere with meaning. • Writer uses grade-level appropriate punctuation, grammar, and spelling.	• Contains correct sentences, usage, grammar, and spelling that make the writer's ideas understandable

STRENGTHS:

WEAKNESSES:

NEXT STEPS:

Teacher Guide

Our resource has been created for ease of use by both TEACHERS and STUDENTS alike.

Introduction

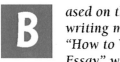

Based on the five-step writing model, our "How to Write an Essay" workbook is an excellent addition to your classroom composition instruction. We include the complete coverage of the four most common types of essays as well as presenting a review of grammar and spelling topics. This material will help prepare your students for your state-mandated written composition exams as well as helping them to view writing as an enjoyable means of recording their thoughts, dreams, and goals.

The "Writing Watchdog" emphasizes important concepts throughout the book. Definitions of important terms and many opportunities to practice the skills being taught also make this book user-friendly and easy to understand. In addition, the objectives used in this book are structured using Bloom's Taxonomy of Learning to ensure educational appropriateness.

How Is Our Resource Organized?

STUDENT HANDOUTS

Reading passages and **activities** (in the form of reproducible worksheets) make up the majority of our resource. The reading passages present important grade-appropriate information and concepts related to the topic. Embedded in each passage are one or more questions that ensure students understand what they have read.

For each reading passage there are **BEFORE YOU READ** activities and **AFTER YOU READ** activities.

- The BEFORE YOU READ activities prepare students for reading by setting a purpose for reading. They stimulate background knowledge and experience, and guide students to make connections between what they know and what they will learn. Important concepts and vocabulary from the chapters are also presented.

- The AFTER YOU READ activities check students' comprehension of the concepts presented in the reading

passage and extend their learning. Students are asked to give thoughtful consideration of the reading passage through creative and evaluative short-answer questions, research, and extension activities.

Writing Tasks are included to further develop students' thinking skills and understanding of the concepts. The **Assessment Rubric** (page 4) is a useful tool for evaluating students' responses to many of the activities in our resource. The **Comprehension Quiz** (page 48) can be used for either a follow-up review or assessment at the completion of the unit.

PICTURE CUES

This resource contains three main types of pages, each with a different purpose and use. A **Picture Cue** at the top of each page shows, at a glance, what the page is for.

 Teacher Guide
- Information and tools for the teacher

 Student Handout
- Reproducible worksheets and activities

 Easy Marking™ Answer Key
- Answers for student activities

EASY MARKING™ ANSWER KEY

Marking students' worksheets is fast and easy with this **Answer Key**. Answers are listed in columns – just line up the column with its corresponding worksheet, as shown, and see how every question matches up with its answer!

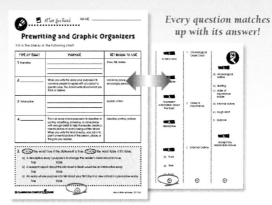

Every question matches up with its answer!

Bloom's Taxonomy* for Reading Comprehension

The activities in this resource engage and build the full range of thinking skills that are essential for students' written composition. Based on the six levels of thinking in Bloom's Taxonomy, assignments are given that challenge students to not only recall what they have read, but move beyond this to understand the text through higher-order thinking. By using higher-order skills of applying, analysing, evaluating, and creating, students become active writers, drawing more meaning from the text, and applying and extending their learning in more sophisticated ways.

This Essay Writing Kit™, therefore, is an effective tool for any Language Arts program. Whether it is used in whole or in part, or adapted to meet individual student needs, this resource provides teachers with the important questions to ask, inspiring students' interest, creativity, and promoting meaningful learning.

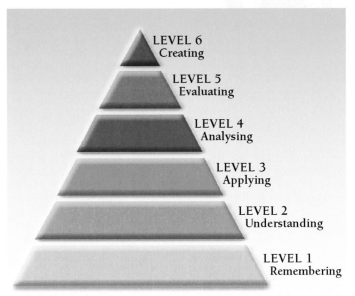

**BLOOM'S TAXONOMY*:
FOR WRITTEN COMPOSITION**

*Bloom's Taxonomy is a widely used tool by educators for classifying learning objectives, and is based on the work of Benjamin Bloom.

Vocabulary

- **essay** – a collection of paragraphs that are all related to the same topic • **prompt** – a suggested topic for an essay or story
- **prewriting** – the first step in the writing process. Prewriting is the step in which the writer brainstorms ideas, makes an outline, and plans the essay • **drafting** – the second step in the writing process. Drafting is the step in which the writer begins to put ideas together as sentences and paragraphs • **revising** – the third step in the writing process. Revising is the step in which the writer changes any words or structure problems in the essay • **proofreading** – the fourth step in the writing process. Proofreading is the step in which the writer looks for any mistakes that have been made
- **publishing** – the fifth step in the writing process. Publishing is the step in which the writer presents the essay to his audience or sends it to a publishing company • **paragraph** – a collection of sentences about the same main topic
- **brainstorming** – a way of coming up with ideas by recording your words and thoughts. The three main methods of brainstorming are listing, clustering, and free-writing • **graphic organizers** – diagrams or drawings which help organize a writer's ideas • **narrative essay** – an essay that tells a story • **persuasive essay** – an essay in which the writer tries to make his readers think as he does about a topic • **informative essay** – an essay which presents information about a topic
- **descriptive essay** – an essay which tells about or describes an object or event • **outline** - an outline is a plan for writing
- **adjectives** – Adjectives describe nouns (people, places, or things) by answering one of these three questions: What kind is it? How many are there? Which one is it? • **objective descriptive essay** – In an objective descriptive essay the writer describes objects, as any person would see them • **subjective descriptive essay** – describes objects and people as the writer sees them • **thesis sentence** – states what you want your readers to know, believe, or understand after reading your essay. It is usually the second or third sentence in the introduction • **verb** – a part of speech that shows action or state-of-being
- **reports or research papers** – other names for an informative essay • **expository essay** – another name for an informative essay • **book reports and biographies** – types of informative essays • **pros and cons** – "Pro" is to agree with a statement, while "con" is to disagree with a statement.

NAME: _____

What is an Essay?

Use one of the words or phrases in the box to complete each statement.

> revising   five paragraphs   conclusion   essay   body
> introduction   publishing   five   graphic organizers   prewriting
> proofreading   purpose   three   drafting

a) An _____ is a collection of paragraphs that are all related to the same topic.

b) Most essays are made up of at least _____ _____.

c) All essays have _____ parts.

d) The first part of an essay is the _____.

e) The second part of the essay is the _____.

f) The final part of the essay is the _____.

g) There are _____ steps in the writing process.

h) The first step in the writing process is _____.

i) _____ _____ are charts or graphs which help organize a writer's ideas.

j) The second step in the writing process is _____.

k) The third step in the writing process is _____.

l) The fourth step in the writing process _____.

m) _____ is the fifth step in the writing process.

n) The reason you choose to write something is your _____.

o) List at least three topics about which you would like to write essays.

_____

_____

NAME: _____

What is an Essay?

Just as a paragraph is a collection of sentences about the same topic, **an essay is a collection of paragraphs that are all related to the same topic. Most essays have five paragraphs organized this way:**

> **Parts of an Essay**
>
> **First paragraph - the introduction**
> **Second, third, and fourth paragraphs - the body of the essay**
> **Fifth paragraph - the conclusion**

Sometimes your teacher may assign a **prompt**, or topic for your essay. Or you may get to choose one on your own. Either way, you should look at your topic and ask yourself, "What do I want my audience to know about this subject?" Your answer will be your purpose for writing. You can easily see that the first two steps in writing an essay are to: 1. choose a topic and 2. choose a purpose for writing.

You have learned that writing is a process made up of several steps. The first step is **prewriting**. After you know your purpose, prewriting is the time to gather and organize the information you want to include in your essay. During prewriting you may jot down notes, make an outline, copy quotations from a book or article, or brainstorm ideas for your essay. As you do this, your teacher may ask you to use graphic organizers to gather the information and put it in a usable form. We will discuss using graphic organizers in a later chapter.

The next step in the writing process is **drafting**. This is the time when you begin to put your ideas into complete sentences on paper. You can share some of the interesting facts you've found through your research or you can make a point about a topic in order to persuade someone to believe as you do. There are several graphic organizers that will help you with the drafting process.

After you have finished the first draft of your essay, you will need to read it very carefully and make any changes in wording or structure that are needed. This process is called **revising** the essay. Your next step will be to **proofread**, or look for and correct any mistakes that you might have made. When you have finished proofreading, your essay is ready to be **published** or presented to your audience.

The Writing Watch Dog says,

"An essay is a short piece of writing that discusses, describes, or analyzes one topic. It can be about anything, and be written in almost any style. It can be serious or funny, straight-forward or symbolic. It can describe personal opinions, or just report information."

After You Read

What is an Essay?

1. **Circle** each phrase that correctly completes each statement.

a) A/an _____ is a collection of sentences about the same topic.

   essay   paragraph   compound sentence

b) A/an _____ is a collection of paragraphs that are all related to the same topic.

   essay   paragraph   compound sentence

c) Writing is a _____ made up of five steps.

   series of words   story   process

d) The step in which you brainstorm ideas, make an outline, and plan what your essay is called _____.

   drafting   prewriting   revising   proofreading   publishing

e) The step in which you look for any mistakes you have made is called _____.

   drafting   prewriting   revising   proofreading   publishing

f) The step in which you change any words or structure problems in your essay is called _____.

   drafting   prewriting   revising   proofreading   publishing

g) The step in which you begin to put your ideas together as sentences and paragraphs is called _____.

   drafting   prewriting   revising   proofreading   publishing

h) The step in which you present your essay to your audience is called _____.

   drafting   prewriting   revising   proofreading   publishing

i) Suggestions of topics for an essay are also called _____.

   titles   names   prompts

j) The reason you write an essay is called your _____ for writing.

   cause   purpose   idea

NAME: _____

Prewriting and Graphic Organizers

Put the letter of the correct term beside the correct meaning:

A prewriting		a graphic organizer that identifies who, what where, when, and why	**1**
B brainstorming		an essay that tells a story	**2**
C graphic organizer		a graphic organizer that lists events in the order they occurred	**3**
D 5 W's Chart		a way of coming up with ideas by recording your words and thoughts.	**4**
E Venn Diagrams		an essay whose purpose is to present information to the reader	**5**
F cause/effect charts		diagrams or drawings which help organize a writer's ideas	**6**
G sequence charts		an essay whose purpose is to convince people to agree with the writer about a specific issue.	**7**
H sensory chart		a graphic organizer that lists the details of the sights, tastes, smells, touches, and sounds of a topic	**8**
I informative essay		the first step in the writing process in which you prepare to write by talking, thinking, and reading about possible writing topics.	**9**
J persuasive essay		graphic organizer often used to compare the likenesses and differences of two or more subjects.	**10**
K narrative essay		a graphic organizer that shows the relationship between two events or conditions when one makes the other happen.	**11**

Prewriting and Graphic Organizers

Prewriting is the first step in the writing process. During prewriting, you begin to prepare to write by talking, thinking, and reading about possible writing topics. There will be times when your teacher assigns a topic for your essay. But many times you will have the chance to choose a topic for yourself. One way to find ideas about a topic is to **brainstorm**. In brainstorming, you write down all of your thoughts about the topic in a set period of time. When you brainstorm, no thought is too silly to write down. Your goal is to list as many ideas related to the subject as you can. As you brainstorm, you should write down everything that comes into your mind about the subject. Often you can use **graphic organizers** to help you brainstorm ideas. You already know that graphic organizers are diagrams or drawings which help you organize your ideas.

There are many kinds of graphic organizers that can help as you prepare to write. You may choose to make a **list** of all the ideas you can think of about a topic. Sometimes, describing the **5 W's** (who, what, where, when, and why) about your topic on a **5 W's Chart** will help you decide which facts to include in your essay. **Sensory Charts** help you think about the sights, smells, tastes, touches, and sounds of an event or object. **Sequence Charts** make it easy to arrange events in the order they occurred. These and other graphic organizers will make your prewriting much easier.

There are four basic types of essays. They are: **narrative essays** that tell a story, **persuasive essays** that try to make your readers think as you do about a topic, **informative essays** that present information about a topic, and **descriptive essays** that tell about or describe an object or event. There are many graphic organizers that are well-suited to each type of essay. Sometimes district or state writing exams will assign a particular type of essay prompt for you to write about. Learning about each kind of essay will certainly help you when your writing exam time comes!

The Writing Watch Dog says, *"Graphic organizers are useful tools which help you visualize concepts, relationships, and facts. They assist you with organizing, interpreting and understanding the parts of an essay."*

NAME: _____

Prewriting and Graphic Organizers

Fill in the blanks in the following chart.

TYPE OF ESSAY	PURPOSE	KEY WORDS TO USE
1. Narrative	_____ _____ _____	show, tell, review
2. _____	When you write this essay your purpose is to convince people to agree with you about a specific issue. You should write about what you think or believe.	convince; prove; encourage; persuade
3. Informative	_____ _____ _____	explain; inform
4. _____	This is an essay whose purpose is to describe or portray something, someone, or some place with enough detail to help the reader create a mental picture of what is being written about. When you write this kind of essay, your job is to paint a mental picture of the person, place, or thing for your readers.	describe, portray, picture

5. Circle the word True if the statement is true. Circle the word False if it's false.

a) A descriptive essay's purpose is to change the reader's mind about an issue.

 True   False

b) A research report about the rain forest in Brazil would be an informative essay.

 True   False

c) An essay whose purpose is to tell about your first day in a new school is a persuasive essay.

 True   False

Drafting and Graphic Organizers

Match each graphic organizer with its description.

INFORMAL OUTLINE

Topic
(Introduction) _____
(sub-point) _____
(sub-point) _____
(Main Point) _____
(sub-point) _____
(sub-point) _____
(sub-point) _____
(Main Point) _____
(sub-point) _____
(sub-point) _____
(Main Point) _____
(sub-point) _____
(sub-point) _____
(Conclusion) _____

CHRONOLOGICAL ORDER CHART

TOPIC –
First, (Introductory Paragraph)
Second, (Body Paragraph)
Third, (Body Paragraph)
Fourth, (Body Paragraph)
Finally, (Conclusion)

ORDER OF IMPORTANCE LADDER

Topic _____

Most Important Idea _____

_____

Supporting Details _____

Summary Idea _____

1. A graphic organizer that arranges the events or topics as they happened.

2. A graphic organizer that arranges ideas by their importance.

3. A graphic organizer that arranges ideas as main topic, supporting details, and closing sentence for each paragraph in the essay.

NAME: _____

Drafting and Graphic Organizers

The second step in the writing process is **drafting**. Writing a **first**, or rough, **draft** is the time to put all your thoughts about the topic on paper. Don't worry too much about spelling or punctuation on the first draft. You'll have time to fix mistakes later. The first draft lets you see how everything fits together. You may want to add or take away some things <u>after</u> you finish the first draft. As you write your first draft, always keep the purpose of the essay in mind. For instance, the purpose of an informative essay is to present facts and ideas about the topic. The purpose of a narrative essay might be to tell about an event, while a descriptive essay's purpose could be to describe a beautiful flower garden. <u>Write your essay with its purpose in mind.</u>

There are several ways to organize your work as you begin your first draft. One good way is to make an **outline. An outline is a plan for writing**. All the important points about your topic are arranged in a logical order in an outline. Outlines can be set up in several ways using graphic organizers. One way of organizing your ideas into an informal outline is to begin by writing your topic at the top of the page. Next, write each main point on the page. Be sure to leave some space between each one. Finally, write the supporting details of each topic underneath it. An example of an outline graphic organizer is shown on the following page. Another good graphic organizer for making an outline is an **Order of Importance Ladder**. On it, you can list the points you want to cover in your essay in the order of their importance. Finally, a **Chronological Outline** is good to use when you are writing about events in history or steps in a process. On a Chronological Outline, the main points or events are listed in the order they occurred.

When you have organized your information in a workable form, it is time to begin writing. Every essay should begin with an **introduction**. In it, you will introduce your main topic and let your readers know what you plan to tell them in your essay. After the introduction, you will write the **body** of your essay. The body is made up of three or more paragraphs containing details about the main topic. Finally, you will finish the essay with a **conclusion** paragraph which sums up all the points you've made about your topic in the introduction and body paragraphs.

Drafting and Graphic Organizers

1. **Complete each statement with a term from the box below.**

> rough draft   informal outline   chronological outline
>
> order of importance ladder   drafting   purpose

a) A graphic organizer that lists the events or steps in a process in the order they occurred is called a _____ _____.

b) The second step in the writing process is called _____.

c) If you want to organize the points in your essay according to how important they are to the topic, you would use an _____.

d) Any type of chart or drawing that helps you gather and sort information for an essay or report is called an _____ _____.

e) A _____ _____ is the result of writing your thoughts and ideas down on paper as sentences and paragraphs.

f) Your reason for writing an essay is called the essay's _____.

2. **Complete the following informal outline using the topic "My Best Year in School".**

Topic: My Best Year in School

(Introduction) _____
(sub-point) _____
(sub-point) _____
(Main Point) _____
(sub-point) _____
(sub-point) _____
(sub-point) _____
(Main Point) _____
(sub-point) _____
(sub-point) _____
(Main Point) _____
(sub-point) _____
(sub-point) _____
(Conclusion) _____

NAME: _____

What is a Descriptive Essay?

1. **Put an X in front of the descriptive essay prompts.**

☐ **a)** Your neighbor has some very strange pets. One day he asks you to babysit his pet raccoon. Write a story about the adventures of babysitting this lovable animal.

☐ **b)** Many television shows are devoted to helping people envision a dream home. Imagine one of these shows has agreed to build your dream home. In a letter, describe your dream home to the show's producers so they will build exactly the home you want.

☐ **c)** Inventions are all around us. Think of an invention that has been especially helpful or harmful to people. Write an essay that explains why.

☐ **d)** Think of a place that you can remember clearly and that is important to you. Think of the sights, sounds, and smells that come rushing back into your memory. Use words to paint a picture of this place that would make a reader feel as if he or she were right there.

☐ **e)** Accidents can happen to anyone. Imagine that you and a friend were playing pitch on the school yard. When you throw your fastball your friend misses the catch and the ball breaks the window of the principal's office! Write an accident report essay describing what happened, how it happened, and who was involved in the accident.

2. **Describing Words:** Adjectives describe **nouns** (people, places, or things) by answering one of these three questions: *What kind is it? How many are there? Which one is it?* Descriptive essays are more interesting when an assortment of adjectives is used in them. Circle at least one adjective in each sentence below and tell which of the three questions it answers.

a) She is my favorite cousin. _____

b) The famous chef served our meal. _____

c) Kittens and cats make excellent pets. _____

d) I like to listen to loud music. _____

e) The little girl is my sister. _____

What is a Descriptive Essay?

A **descriptive essay** is an essay whose purpose is to describe or portray something, someone, or some place with enough detail to help the reader create a mental picture of it. **When you write a descriptive essay, your job is to paint a mental picture of the person, place, or thing for your readers.**

There are two kinds of descriptive essays. The first kind is an **objective essay**. In an objective descriptive essay the writer describes objects, as any person would see them – color, shape, length, height, width, weight, etc. Objective essays do not contain any of the writer's likes or dislikes or feelings about the object being described. A good example of an <u>objective descriptive essay is a Police Report of an Accident.</u> The policeman does not say whether or not one of the cars is his/her favorite color or whether or not the accident happened in front of the best skateboard store in town. These are personal likes and dislikes. The second kind of descriptive essay is an **impressionistic or subjective essay.** These kinds of essays describe objects and people as the writer sees them. They rely on the writer's five senses to paint a picture in the reader's mind.

The first step in prewriting for a good descriptive essay is planning. Your planning should include: 1. choosing a topic (if you are given a choice); 2. gathering information about the topic; and 3. using a graphic organizer to map out the structure of the descriptive essay.

There are several types of graphic organizers suitable for descriptive essays. A **Five Senses Graphic Organizer** is an excellent one during your prewriting work on a descriptive essay. You can record how an object or event affected your own five senses. Another good organizer for descriptive essays is a **Spider Map Graphic Organizer**. On it, you write the main topic of the essay on the body of the spider and supporting details on each of the spider's eight legs.

It is very important to remember that descriptive essays should contain colorful language. Try to use as many adjectives as you can in your essay. Descriptive essays do not tell a story, convince someone to think a certain way, or present a report about something. **In a descriptive essay, your purpose is to describe as many characteristics of a person, place, thing, or feeling as you can.**

The Writing Watch Dog says,
"Great descriptive essays use detailed observations and descriptions to project complete pictures into the minds of your audience."

What is a Descriptive Essay?

1. **Complete the following Spider Map Organizer for a descriptive essay about your favorite dessert.**

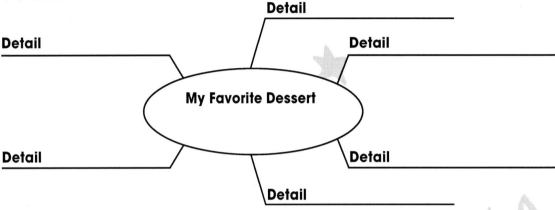

2. **Complete each statement**

   a) The purpose of a descriptive essay is to _____.

   b) The two types of descriptive essays are _____ and _____.

   c) Descriptive essays should contain a great deal of colorful _____.

   d) The first step of any prewriting process should be _____.

   e) When you write a descriptive essay, your job is to paint a _____ _____ of the topic.

   f) A good graphic organizer to use for a descriptive essay is a _____ Map.

Things to Remember When You Write a Descriptive Essay about an event:

Think of an event that you want to describe.

- Why is this particular event important?
- What were you doing?
- What other things were happening around you? Is there anything specific that stands out in your mind?
- Where were objects located in relation to where you were?
- How did the surroundings remind you of other places you have been?
- What sights, smells, sounds, and tastes were in the air?
- Did the sights, smells, sounds, and tastes remind you of anything?

- What were you feeling at that time?
- Has there been a time in which you have felt this way before?
- What do you want the reader to feel after reading the paper?
- What types of words and images can convey this feeling?
- Can you think of another situation that was similar to the one you are writing about? How can it help explain what you are writing about?
- Is there enough detail in your essay to create a mental image for the reader?

Writing a Descriptive Essay

Put the letter of the correct term in the blank in front of its meaning.

A descriptive essay

B topic sentence

C thesis sentence

D introduction

E body

F conclusion

G describing words

1. the final paragraph of a descriptive essay. It should restate the thesis of the essay and summarize the points made by the writer.

2. the first paragraph of a descriptive essay. It should grab the reader's attention and state what the essay will be about.

3. an essay whose purpose is to describe or portray something, someone, or some place with enough detail to help the reader create a mental picture of what is being written about.

4. the second, third, and fourth paragraphs of a descriptive essay. Each paragraph should discuss one or more of the points stated by the writer in the thesis statement.

5. adjectives that answer "What kind is it? How many are there? Which one is it?

6. should grab your reader's attention. It is usually the first sentence in a paragraph.

7. states what you want your readers to know, believe, or understand after reading your essay. It is usually the second or third sentence in the introduction.

2. **Circle every adjective in each sentence. The number at the end of the sentence tells how many adjectives it contains.**

a) It was a dark and stormy night. (2)

b) I have two brothers and four sisters. (2)

c) The shaggy dog ran after the fluffy cat. (2)

d) He drove a red car with black seats. (2)

e) Dad gave me ten dollars and fifteen cents. (2)

Writing a Descriptive Essay

All descriptive essays: 1. present one, clear picture in the reader's mind; 2. can be objective or subjective; and 3. have one purpose which is to help the reader visualize the things that are being described. Therefore, it is necessary for all descriptive essays to contain a number of descriptive words and phrases.

The first paragraph in your descriptive essay is the introduction. This paragraph should have four or five powerful sentences that introduce the topic you are describing to your readers.

The first sentence of your introductory paragraph is your chance to <u>grab</u> your readers' attention. One way to do this is to make a general statement about your topic. For example, if your topic is your favorite season of the year, you might say: "<u>Every summer I come down with a strange illness called "outside-itis.</u>" **This sentence will be your topic sentence.** It grabs your readers' attention and lets them know that the paragraph is going to be about spring. **The topic sentence is the first sentence in your introductory paragraph.**

The **thesis statement** follows the topic sentence in the introductory paragraph. Remember that topic or grabber sentences catch the reader's eye and tell what the <u>paragraph</u> is about. **A thesis sentence goes a bit further. A thesis sentence states what you want your readers to know, believe, or understand after reading your essay.** In our essay about your favorite season of the year, the thesis sentence could be, "<u>Each of my senses is filled up with the sights, sounds, smells, tastes, and feelings of summer.</u>" The sentence following the thesis sentence should give more information about it, and the fourth and fifth sentences should summarize your thoughts and transition to the next paragraph.

The second, third, and fourth paragraphs of a descriptive essay are the **body** of your writing. In our seasons essay, each paragraph could describe how spring affects one or more of your five senses.

The last paragraph of a descriptive essay is the **conclusion**. In it, you should <u>restate the thesis sentence of your first paragraph</u>, "Each of my senses is filled up with the sights, sounds, smells, tastes, and feelings of summer," and then summarize all the reasons you have presented for loving summer.

The Writing Watch Dog says,
"Here are some important tips to remember about writing descriptive essays:
1. Take time to brainstorm.
2. Choose your words carefully.
3. Use vivid, colorful language.
4. Use your five senses!
5. Clearly describe your thoughts to your readers.
6. Leave your reader with a clear impression of what you think.
7. Be organized!

After You Read

Writing a Descriptive Essay

1. Use the descriptive essay prompt, "My Favorite Hobby" and write a topic sentence, two or three supporting sentences, and a summary sentence for each paragraph on the Essay Map below.

INTRODUCTION PARAGRAPH # 1
Topic Sentence
Thesis Statement

INTRODUCTION PARAGRAPH # 2
Topic Sentence

Support Support Support Support

INTRODUCTION PARAGRAPH # 3
Topic Sentence

Support Support Support Support

INTRODUCTION PARAGRAPH # 4
Topic Sentence

Support Support Support Support

CONCLUSION PARAGRAPH # 5
Topic Sentence

Support Support Support Support

NAME: _____

What is a Narrative Essay?

1. **Choose the correct term or phrase to complete each statement.**

narrative essay	action verbs	"be" verbs	sequence	sensory
	"mind movie"	powerful		

a) "Is, am, were, was, are, be, being, and been" are all _____.

b) An essay that tells about the writer's experiences and is written in the form of a story is called a _____.

c) When events are written about in the order they happened we say they are written in _____.

d) A good way to plan a narrative essay is to project a _____ _____ in the mind of your listener or reader.

e) Words that help your readers picture what the characters are doing in your essay are called _____ _____.

f) Words that appeal to the reader's five senses are called _____ words.

g) A narrative essay should have many _____ verbs in it.

2. **Circle the action verbs in the following sentences. (Some sentences may have more than one action verb.)**

a) The horse galloped across the grass.

b) The kids dodged the ball and raced inside the school.

c) The fire crackled in the basement in a pile of rags.

d) Soldiers marched by the people and saluted them.

e) Casey sings in the chorus at school.

f) I twisted and turned in the chair for ten minutes.

g) Ben raced to the store.

h) The alarm clock buzzed like a bumblebee and startled us awake.

What is a Narrative Essay?

You have already learned that a **narrative essay** tells about the writer's experiences and is written in the form of a story. A narrative essay can also be based on someone else's experiences and can be fact or fiction. Many of the greatest books of all time are written as narrative essays.

You should follow the five steps of the writing process as you plan and write a narrative essay. Your first actions in writing a narrative essay should be to: 1. Identify the experience that you want to write about; 2. Think about why the experience will be important to your audience; 3. Spend time thinking about the details of the experience; and 4. Create an outline of the basic parts of the narrative essay's contents.

When you write a narrative essay you will **tell about events in the order that they happened.** An excellent way to write a narrative essay is to pretend that you are describing a movie to a friend. Your goal is to have your friend see a "mind movie" in his head. Think of all the details that you need to add to make the movie clear and sensible. You can't just say, "They got into a large rocket ship." You might say, "Dad and Mom ran up the stairway of a huge, silver spaceship with alien-looking symbols drawn on its sides." Two very good graphic organizers to use during the prewriting for a narrative essay are the **Storyboard** and the **Skeleton Plan**.

Another very important tip to remember when you compose a narrative essay is to use **strong verbs.** You recall that **a verb is a part of speech that shows action or state-of-being.** "State-of-being" verbs are any forms of the word, "be" – is, am, were, was, are, be, being, been." "State-of-being" verbs are verbs that state that something **IS**. "State-of-being" verbs are **NOT** powerful verbs. In fact, one author says that, "BE verbs are boring!" <u>Always try to limit the number of "be" verbs you use in your essays.</u>

Action verbs describe the action or behavior of somebody or something. Words such as "giggled", "screamed", "raced", "tiptoed", and "whispered" are all action verbs. Action verbs keep your audience interested in your writing and help them see the story in their minds. "Show, don't tell" is advice that every good writer should follow. **The objective of writing a narrative essay is to make the reader feel as if he is seeing the story unfold before him.** Good writers use action and dialog to show what a character is thinking, saying, and doing. Showing can be done by: 1. writing scenes; 2. describing the actions of the characters; 3. revealing character through dialog; and 4. using the five senses when possible.

<u>Finally, a narrative essay will almost always communicate a central main idea or a lesson learned by one or more main characters.</u> A narrative essay is not just a retelling of the events in someone's life. A narrative story teaches a lesson or makes a very important point.

The Writing Watch Dog says,
"Rather than just telling your readers what happens, use vivid details and descriptions to recreate the experience for them."

What is a Narrative Essay?

1. A narrative essay tells a story. Using the narrative prompt, "The Day When I Stood Up for My Beliefs", fill in the Skeleton Plan graphic Organizer. You may need to use another sheet of paper if you run out of room. Think about who would enjoy hearing or reading this essay. What is your purpose? In what order did the day's event progress?

SKELETON PLAN

Topic?		Audience?	
Purpose?		Format?	

QUESTIONS	ANSWERS	DETAILS
What happened first?		
What happened second?		

2. **Put an X in front of the narrative essay prompts.**

☐ **a)** Think of a day in your life when everything seemed to be going wrong. Tell about it.

☐ **b)** Describe your favorite room in your house.

☐ **c)** What is one of the funniest things that has ever happened to you? Retell the event as completely as you can.

☐ **d)** The school board of your district is considering making the school day longer by adding an extra hour. Your job is to write an essay either for or against this idea.

☐ **e)** Suppose one day you found a flying carpet. Write an essay telling what happened.

Writing a Narrative Essay

1. Use the narrative essay prompt below to help you fill in the outline. You will need to use a copy of the **Simple Outline Graphic Organizer** that is included in this book for your work.

> **NARRATIVE ESSAY PROMPT**
> **You and your mother are home alone when suddenly a tornado is spotted coming toward your house. Tell about your experience.**

Title of Your Essay_____

Introduction (first paragraph)

-"Grab" your audience's attention (first sentence) _____

-Thesis statement (second or third statement) _____

-Introduce supporting ideas (fourth or fifth sentence) _____

Body of Essay (paragraphs 2, 3, &4)

First Supporting Idea (second paragraph)

-Topic sentence (first sentence) _____

-Discussion & ideas (next two or three sentences) _____

-Transition to next paragraph (last sentence) _____

Second Supporting Idea (third paragraph)

-Topic sentence (first sentence) _____

-Discussion & ideas (next two or three sentences) _____

-Transition to next paragraph (last sentence) _____

Third Supporting Idea (fourth paragraph)

-Topic sentence (first sentence) _____

-Discussion & ideas (next two or three sentences) _____

-Transition to next paragraph (last sentence) _____

Conclusion (fifth paragraph)

- Transition, statement reflecting back on thesis (first sentence) _____

- Restate key points (second, third & fourth sentences)_____

- Ending statement that summarizes or provokes thought (fifth sentence) _____

NAME: _____

Writing a Narrative Essay

Narrative essays often are about the personal experiences of the writer. These experiences are presented to the reader in story form. Good narrative essays are well-developed. That means that they are easy to understand and have enough details. Below are some ways to write a well-developed narrative essay:

Ways to Write a Well-Developed Essay

1. Use examples and illustrations
2. Use anecdotes (short stories related to the topic)
3. Use what people say
4. Define words
5. Describe the topic
6. Look at causes and effects
7. Compare and Contrast
8. Tell the order in which events happened

When you begin prewriting activities for a narrative essay, be sure that it has a unified purpose or that the essay is about only one main topic. All the sentences in all of the paragraphs must relate to that one purpose or topic. Always try to keep this in mind as you brainstorm, outline, or list.

Another of the most important goals in drafting a narrative essay is to make sure that you get all your ideas down on paper in some kind of sequential order.

There are several good graphic organizers to help you with sequential order as you write your narrative essay. A Timeline Graphic Organizer and a Hierarchy Chart are two very good ones.

The best way to learn to write a good narrative essay is to do just that – write one! Below you will find some very good tips about writing a good narrative essay:

- Begin the introductory paragraph of the essay with a general statement about the topic.
- Be sure to give details about the people and events in the essay. Using a Word Picture Chart will help you include descriptive language. A great way to make sure that you include all the details you need for a colorful, interesting essay is to plan before you write.
- Each of the body paragraphs should relate back to the main topic in the first paragraph. Remember that a narrative essay is basically a story.
- The final paragraph is the conclusion. It should restate the main topic that was introduced in the introduction.

The Writing Watch Dog says,
"Writing a narrative essay is as easy as writing a story!"

Writing a Narrative Essay

1. **Fill in each blank with a word or phrase from the lesson.**

a) A narrative essay tells a _____.

b) Many times, a narrative essay includes the personal _____ of the writer.

c) Well developed narrative essays are easy to _____ and have lots of _____.

d) A good narrative essay has a _____ purpose which means that the essay is about _____ main topic.

e) Usually, the events in a narrative essay are presented in _____ order or the order in which they happened.

2. One way to make your essay more interesting is to use sensory words. You learned that sensory words are words used to describe the five senses: seeing, smelling, hearing, tasting, and touching. A good guide to help you think of sensory words to use is the Word Picture Organizer. Use the same narrative prompt, **"You and your mother are home alone when suddenly a tornado is spotted coming toward your house". Tell about your experience, and fill out the following Word Picture Organizer.**

SIGHTS	SOUNDS	TASTES	SMELLS	TEXTURES	OTHER IMPORTANT DETAILS

What is an Informative Essay?

1. **Put an "I" in front of each <u>informative essay title</u>.**

☐ **a)** The Story of Paul Bunyan and Babe the Blue Ox

☐ **b)** The Causes of the Civil War

☐ **c)** Why You Should Vote for Tim Hall for Class President

☐ **d)** The Animals of Australia

☐ **e)** A Report about Tales of a 4th Grade Nothing by Judy Blume

2. Use the informative prompt, "Animals in My State", and complete this KWL organizer.

K What I **Know**	W **What** I Want to Learn	L What I Have **Learned**

What is an Informative Essay?

The next kind of essay we will study is called an **Informative** or an **Expository Essay**. Don't let the word "expository" scare you. An expository essay is simply the explanation of a subject. An expository essay is fact-based, not opinion-based. Very often, you will need to do research in the library or online. When you write an expository essay you will need to give information, explain the topic, or define something. Sometimes, expository essays are called reports or research papers.

You will be asked to write an informative or expository essay for one or more of the following reasons: 1. to explain a process step-by-step; 2. to analyze events, ideas, written works, or objects; 3. to tell how to do something; or 4. to explain or describe a historical event.

You may get to choose the topic of your informative essay or your teacher might assign a topic to you. Either way, be sure that your topic is not too broad. Suppose you wanted to write about Los Angeles, California. It is a very large city and also a very broad topic. Perhaps, it might be easier to write about one part of the city such as the movie studios. A **KWL Organizer** will help you narrow your topic and decide which parts to include in your informative essay. A KWL Organizer asks you to list what you already **know** about the topic, what you want to know about the topic, and what you have already **learned** about the topic.

An informative essay is set up exactly like the descriptive and narrative essays are. The first paragraph introduces the main topic while the second, third, and fourth tell more about it. Finally, the fifth paragraph restates the purpose of the paper and concludes with a summary of all the facts about the topic.

The **3-2-1 Planner** is a graphic organizer that helps you gather all your information for an informative essay. The "3-2-1" stands for three key ideas, two details for each idea, all in one topic. The 3-2-1 Planner helps you organize your essay into three parts (beginning, middle, and end) and plan two details for each part. Using this planner will help you make sure that all the information you need for your essay is included and that you have left out any unrelated information.

The Writing Watch Dog says,
"Keep in mind that an expository essay is one that:
1. explains a subject
2. tells the steps of a process
3. presents ideas in logical order or correct sequence
The key words in an expository essay prompt will be "explain" or "tell how".

What is an Informative Essay?

Sometimes, you will need to write an informative essay to tell someone how to do something. Use the prompt, "Getting ready for a two-week vacation", and complete the **Steps in a Process Organizer** below.

Steps in a Process

First

Second

Third

Fourth

Fifth

Before You Read

Writing an Informative Essay

1. **Circle** the correct term to complete each statement.

   a) An essay that presents information about a particular topic is called a(an) _____.

   persuasive essay   narrative essay   informative essay   descriptive essay

   b) Each informative essay should begin with a _____ _____.

   capital letter   thesis statement   body paragraph   conclusion paragraph

   c) Before you write an informative essay, you should develop a(an) _____ of all the important facts that must be included in it.

   alphabetical list   outline   graphic organizer full of

   d) An informative essay presents many facts to the reader. It is very important for the writer to document the _____ of all the facts included in an informative essay.

   pictures   sources   locations in the library

2. **A report about a famous person is a great example of an informative essay. Use the Biography Chart below to develop an outline about the life of Albert Einstein.**

   Biography about:

   Famous because:

   Birthplace:

   Early Life:

   Education

   Major Life Events:

   Other Information:

   Quote:

   Research sources:

Writing an Informative Essay

An **informative** or **expository essay** is written to present facts about a topic. **Book reports, biographies, and research reports** are all types of informative essays. Informative essays are most often written to: 1. to explain a process step-by-step; 2. to analyze events, ideas, written works, or objects; 3. to tell how to do something; or 4. to explain or describe a historical event.

As with all essays, the first step in the writing process is prewriting. During the prewriting period, you should complete your research, record your sources of information, and make an outline of the important points you want to make in the essay. There are several good graphic organizers to use that will help you organize your ideas before you begin writing.

The next step in writing an informative essay is drafting or putting your thoughts down as sentences and paragraphs. Your essay should have five or more paragraphs. The first paragraph is the introduction. It begins with a good topic sentence that "grabs" your reader's attention. Suppose your teacher asked you to write an informative essay about George Washington. Your topic sentence might be "The United States has had over forty presidents, but I believe that the first one was the best!" This is a good way of getting your reader's attention.

The next sentence should be the **thesis statement** that should tell the main idea of the entire essay, such as, "George Washington was better qualified to lead the United States than anyone who has come after him." The next three sentences in the introduction should introduce three main points about George Washington such as, "Washington was especially well-educated in the theories of government. He was an excellent military leader. His main hope for the future was that the 13 colonies would become free from English rule." Finally, the last sentence should lead into the next paragraph.

The next three paragraphs are called the **body** of the informative essay. In each paragraph, you should choose one of the three main points you mentioned in the introduction paragraph and discuss it. For example, "Washington was especially well-educated in the theories of government." could be the topic sentence for paragraph # 2. Each paragraph relates back to the thesis statement, "George Washington was better qualified to lead the United States than anyone who has come after him."

Finally, the fifth paragraph should be the **conclusion**. Its topic sentence could be a restatement of the topic sentence of the introduction, "For these reasons, history has proven that George Washington was the best man ever to be president of the United States." The next three sentences should be concluding remarks about Washington and the last sentence should be a restatement of the thesis sentence. The **Introduction Triangle and the Body Block** graphic organizers on the following page will help illustrate how an informative essay is written.

After You Read

Writing an Informative Essay

1. Write an introduction to an informative essay about *Charlotte's Web*.

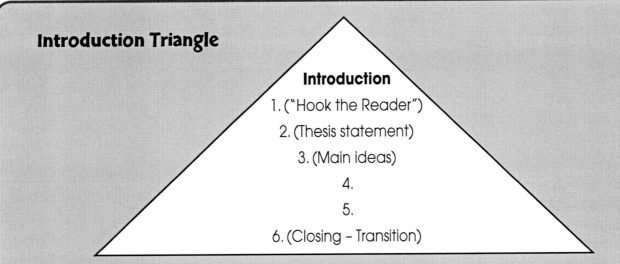

Introduction Triangle

Introduction

1. ("Hook the Reader")

2. (Thesis statement)

3. (Main ideas)

4.

5.

6. (Closing – Transition)

Body Block Now write the body paragraphs using the hints that have been provided:

Paragraph # 2: This book is a story about a girl named Fern and a pig named Wilbur.

Paragraph # 3: However, the most important friend Wilbur would ever have was a simple gray spider named Charlotte.

Paragraph # 4: Charlotte alone had the power to save Wilbur's life.

Conclusion Triangle

Final Paragraph

Summary Statements –

One or two sentences.

Who would have thought that the runt in the litter would be "Some Pig" and "Radiant"?

Closing statement.

NAME: _____

What is a Persuasive Essay?

1. **Circle** each persuasive essay prompt below.

a) Teachers should assign at least two hours of homework to each student every day.

b) All violent television programs should be taken off the air immediately.

c) Describe the best vacation you ever had.

d) Tell why someone in your family deserves a $25,000 award for their hard work.

e) Write a story about the first astronauts to land on a Mars space station.

Answer each question with a complete sentence.

2. What is the purpose of a persuasive essay?

_____

3. What is the difference between a narrative essay and a persuasive essay?

_____

4. What do you think "pro" and "con" mean?

_____

5. **Make a list of five problems that you would like to convince others to help you solve.**

a) _____

b) _____

c) _____

d) _____

e) _____

What is a Persuasive Essay?

The purpose of a persuasive essay is to change your readers' minds and make them think like you do about a topic. The first step in prewriting a persuasive essay is planning. Your planning should include: 1. choosing a topic; gathering information about the topic; and using a graphic organizer to map out the structure of the persuasive essay.

When you choose a topic for your persuasive essay, you will have to decide how you feel about the issue that is being discussed. One good way to do this is to complete a **Pro and Con T-Chart.** "Pro" means that you agree with a statement or that you are for an action, while "con" means that you disagree with a statement or that you disagree with an action. You will find a Pro and Con T-Chart on the following page.

As you prepare to write a persuasive essay, you will find that you need to study both sides of the issue being considered if you hope to make people believe as you do about the topic. The Pro and Con T-Chart is one good way to consider both sides. Another is using a **Five Finger Planner.** You may use the Five Finger Planner graphic organizer that comes with this book or you may want to trace the outline of your own hand. On the palm of the hand outline, write the "pro" side of the question being considered. Then on each finger write one reason why people should be "pro" or for this statement. If you are going to convince your audience to be "con" or against an issue, write "con" on the palm of the hand outline and then write one reason why your audience should be against the question being considered on each finger. You will find a shortened version of the five finger planner on the following page.

When you begin to write a persuasive essay it is especially important that you make sure all the facts you use are correct! Even though you will be trying to change someone's feelings about an issue, you must always use the facts of the matter as your tools. Using doubtful or untrue information in order to persuade people to change their minds is the same as telling them a lie. Be careful to be truthful when you write persuasive essays. Of course, you should always include your own feelings about the topic and then try to persuade your audience to believe as you do.

The Writing Watch Dog says, *"When you write a persuasive essay, you are trying to make the audience think like you do about a topic or question."*

What is a Persuasive Essay?

1. Using the question, "Should two hours be added to the school day schedule?",
    list its "pros" and "cons".

Pro and Con T-Chart
QUESTION TO BE ANSWERED
Should two hours be added to the school day schedule?

    Pros   **Cons**

2. **Circle** the word True if the statement is true. **Circle** the word False if it's false.

    a) The writer tries to change the audience's minds in a descriptive essay.

    True   False

    b) One of the first things to do when you are preparing to write a persuasive essay is to
    choose a good topic.

    True   False

    c) It is not very important to study both sides of the issue or topic before you begin writing
    a persuasive essay.

    True   False

    d) Politicians often present persuasive essays and speeches in an effort to make the
    audience vote for them.

    True   False

    e) The truth should not be a major concern of yours when you write a persuasive essay.

    True   False

© CLASSROOM COMPLETE PRESS

NAME: _____

Writing a Persuasive Essay

1. **Put the letter of the correct term in the blank in front of its meaning.**

A persuasive essay

B topic sentence

C thesis statement

D introductory paragraph

E body paragraphs

F conclusion or summary paragraph

the first three paragraphs that follow the introductory paragraph.	**1**
The last paragraph in a persuasive essay.	**2**
An essay written to change your readers' minds and make them think like you do about a topic.	**3**
The second or third sentence in the introductory paragraph. It identifies the purpose of the essay or previews its main ideas	**4**
The first sentence in a paragraph. It usually "grabs" the reader's attention in some way.	**5**
The first paragraph in a persuasive essay. It introduces the topic and gives the reader an idea about the content of the essay.	**6**

2. Use the "Here's What I Think…" graphic organizer below to plan the introductory paragraph of a persuasive essay using the prompt, **"Kids do NOT spend too much time watching television!"**

Here's What I Think…

Introduction - Position Statement

Thesis Statement

Reasons

Closing/Transitions:

NAME: _____

Writing a Persuasive Essay

Now it is time to write a persuasive essay about an issue or problem that you'd like to solve. Many times, a persuasive essay poses a question which must be answered. Your job is to get your audience to choose the answer you believe is best. As you get ready to write your persuasive essay, the graphic organizer entitled, "**Pick a Problem**" may be helpful to you. This graphic organizer asks you to identify a problem that needs to be solved and then asks several questions about the problem such as, "What is wrong? What should change?; "What should be done now?"; "What can be done over time?"; "How can you get others to join in?"; "What good things might come of your plan?"; and "What might go wrong?" You will get a chance to use the "Pick a Problem" organizer later in this chapter.

The first paragraph in your essay is called the introduction or introductory paragraph. It should have four or five powerful sentences that introduce your topic to your audience. The first sentence of a persuasive essay should be your "attention-getting" sentence. This is your chance to grab your audience's attention. You might do this with a general statement about the issue you have chosen. The second sentence of a persuasive essay's introduction should narrow the first sentence or give more information about your topic. The third sentence of a persuasive essay's introduction should state your feelings about the topic or question. This is your thesis statement. The fourth sentence should outline your reasons for believing as you do. And the fifth sentence of a persuasive essay's introduction should summarize your thesis and transition to the next paragraph.

The next three paragraphs are called the **body** of your persuasive paragraph. Each paragraph should begin with a topic sentence that refers back to one of the reasons you believe as you do about the issue you are discussing. The following sentences give you an opportunity to present your evidence or proof of what you are saying is true and needed at this time.

The fifth paragraph is called the **conclusion paragraph**. The first sentence should refer back to your thesis statement in paragraph # 1. The following three sentences should summarize the body paragraphs you have written and the last sentence should be a restatement or rewording of the topic sentence of paragraph # 1. An outline of a persuasive paragraph should look like this:

1. **Body – Supporting Paragraph 1**
   Topic Sentence
   Supporting Sentences (3)
   Transition/conclusion

2. **Body – Supporting Paragraph 2**
   Topic Sentence
   Supporting Sentences (3)
   Transition/conclusion

3. **Body – Supporting Paragraph 3**
   Topic Sentence
   Supporting Sentences (3)
   Transition/conclusion

4. **Conclusion Paragraph**
   Transition into the conclusion by restating Thesis/ Position Statement Summarize your body paragraphs: Final "clincher" sentence that leaves the reader satisfied with your argument.

Writing a Persuasive Essay

1. Use the Persuasive Essay Outline below to compose a persuasive essay using the following prompt. **You and your classmates want to visit a special amusement park on a field trip. Write a persuasive essay telling your teacher the reasons why visiting this park on a field trip would be a great idea. Try to convince your teacher to accept your choice.**

Persuasive Essay Outline

Essay Title _____

Introduction - Position Statement
Thesis Statement:_____
Reasons (3):_____
Closing/Transition: _____

Body – Supporting Paragraph 1
Topic Sentence_____
Supporting Sentences (3) _____
Transition/conclusion _____

Body – Supporting Paragraph 2
Topic Sentence_____
Supporting Sentences (3) _____
Transition/conclusion _____

Body – Supporting Paragraph 3
Topic Sentence_____
Supporting Sentences (3) _____
Transition/conclusion _____

Conclusion Paragraph
Transition into the conclusion by restating Thesis/ Position Statement _____
Summarize your body paragraphs: _____
Final "clincher" sentence that leaves the reader satisfied with your argument: __

NAME: _____

Revising, Proofreading and Editing

Fill in each blank with a complete sentence.

1. **What is the third step in the writing process?**

_____

2. **Describe what it means to proofread something you have written.**

_____

3. **What are the three parts of revision?**

_____

4. **Why do you think that "rest" is the first stage of proofreading?**

_____

5. **Proofread the following paragraph and see if you can find __20__ mistakes in it.** Circle **each mistake. Then rewrite the paragraph on the lines below.**

The christmas surprise

Last christmas was the best hollyday that i ever had? all of my famly were together in one place for the first tim in yers. Dad was werking on a pressent for Mom and me in the grage. My bother, Jim, was home on leaf from the Army. Grandpa and Grandma was coming to see us on Christmas day. it don't matter how meny presents you get, love is the most special present of all. Haveing everone heer in one house made this the best holiday ever!

_____

_____

_____

_____

_____

_____

_____

Revising, Proofreading and Editing

When you have finished drafting an essay it is time for you to begin the **revision process**. **Revision is the third step in the writing process and simply means, "to look at again".** Revision has three parts – 1. rest; 2. reread; and 3. make changes. "Rest" means that you should leave the essay alone for several hours or even a day before you begin the reviewing process. When it is time to look at the essay again, you can reread it silently or even reread it aloud. Look for any changes that need to be made in the wording, capitalization, punctuation, and meaning. You may also need to add or change some words around when you reread. Finally, go ahead and make the changes that need to be made. The Revision Checklist below is an excellent tool to use when you revise an essay:

Revision Checklist	Yes	No
1. Have you stated the main idea or thesis in your introduction?	_____	_____
2. Did you follow the directions in your writing prompt?	_____	_____
3. Are your paragraphs clear and on topic?	_____	_____
4. Did you write a good introduction paragraph?	_____	_____
5. Have you written a good conclusion paragraph?	_____	_____
6. Is the essay organized well?	_____	_____
7. Did you use transitions between the paragraphs?	_____	_____
8. Did you "grab" or "hook" the reader in the introduction?	_____	_____
9. Did the conclusion paragraph restate the thesis?	_____	_____
10. Does each paragraph in the body address one of the main ideas you listed in the introduction?	_____	_____

Now comes the time when you will be looking for even the tiniest mistakes in your essay. **Proofreading and editing are fourth steps in the writing process. Proofreading means that you reread your writing to look very carefully for any mistakes that you've made in spelling, punctuation, word choice, or sentence choice.** You may even want to ask someone else to proofread your essay for you. However you decide to proofread, **the final goal is the fifth step in the writing process which is to have a perfect essay to present to your teacher or your audience**.

The Writing Watch Dog says, *"Be sure to follow these Proofreading Pointers!"*

1. Check for correct spelling. Use a dictionary if a word doesn't look right.
2. Check for correct use of capital letters. Always begin a sentence with a capital letter.
3. Check for correct punctuation including periods, commas, apostrophes, and quotation marks.
4. Check for correct word choice.
5. Make sure that the subject and predicate agree in number.

Revising, Proofreading and Editing

1. **Circle** **the correct answer in each sentence.**

   a) (Its) (It's) time for lunch.

   b) I'm afraid (its) (it's) going to be a long trip in the car with my baby brother.

   c) (Its) (It's) five o'clock and no one is here!

   d) (They're) (There) (Their) going on vacation next month with (they're) (there) (their) grandparents.

   e) I looked and looked and (they're) (there) (their) it was.

   f) Mom and Dad said (they're) (there) (their) bringing home a surprise.

2. **Add the correct punctuation or capitalization to each sentence.**

   a) alex and sam read how to eat fried worms by thomas rockwell.

   b) i met kim while I was staying at the grand hotel in michigan.

   c) dr. jones said, "you'll be fine if you and joey don't get into any more fights!"

   d) We bought milk eggs bacon and bread at the store.

   e) Sam can you help me with this package?

   f) Kwan lives in Saratoga New York.

   g) My grandmother's favorite song is Rock Around the Clock.

3. **Circle** **the correct word in each sentence.**

   a) (Whos) (Who's) at the door?

   b) She (couldn't) (couldnt) hear her (childrens) (children's) cries for help.

   c) The (woman's) (womans') coats hung in the hall closet.

   d) I (won't) (wont) know about my grade until the mail comes.

   e) The boys (work) (works) on the project every day.

   f) We (learn) (learns) about English grammar in our class.

   g) Mr. Hill and Ms. Long (teach) (teaches) fourth grade at our school.

You are holding a family photograph. As you look at the photograph you are suddenly transported back into the time and setting of the picture. **Describe the picture and explain the interesting things that happened on the day the picture was taken.**

_____
_____
_____
_____
_____
_____
_____
_____
_____
_____

📝 Writing Task # 2

More and more violence is being seen on television programs each year. Many people believe that this violence is harmful to children. They want to take all the violent programs including cartoons, off the air. **Decide what you think about taking violent programs off the air. Then write a five paragraph essay about your thoughts. Remember that you are trying to convince your readers to think as you do about this topic.**

_____
_____
_____
_____
_____
_____

📝 Writing Task # 3

Think about where people live. People live in small towns, large towns, or even big cities. Some people live on farms or in houses in the country. Think about where it is best to live and why. **Choose the one place where you would like to live and write a persuasive essay giving reasons why you think it is the best.**

_____
_____
_____
_____
_____
_____
_____
_____
_____
_____

- -

📝 Writing Task # 4

Each year millions of tourists visit Florida.
Before you begin writing, think about Florida as a place to go on vacation.
Now write to explain why Florida is a popular place to go on vacation.

_____
_____
_____
_____
_____
_____
_____
_____

Writing Task # 5

Think about the last time you attended a special event such as a concert, a fair, or a sports event. **Write a descriptive essay telling what it was like to be there and include sights, sounds, and smells that will make the reader feel he or she is there with you.**

_____

_____

_____

_____

_____

_____

_____

_____

Writing Task # 6

If you had one thousand dollars to spend, how would you spend it? Would you buy something, save it, share it...? What is the very best thing you could do with one thousand dollars? **Explain your choice in a five-paragraph essay with three reasons, and include specific details, examples, and explanations to support your argument.**

_____

_____

_____

_____

_____

_____

NAME: _____

Crossword

Word List

adjectives
biography
brainstorming
drafting
expository
graphic
informative
narrative
objective
outline
paragraph
prewriting
prompt
proofreading
pros
publishing
reports
revision
verb

Across

5. An essay that presents information about a topic
6. A type of informative essay
7. The first steps in the writing process
8. Words that describe nouns
10. A way of coming up with ideas by recording your words and thoughts
13. _____ organizers
15. The third step in the writing process
16. A collection of sentences about the same main topic
18. A plan for writing is an _____
19. A type of descriptive essay

Down

1. Another name for an informative essay
2. The fourth step in the writing process
3. The fifth step in the writing process
4. Book _____
9. The second step in the writing process
11. An essay that tells a story
12. A suggested topic for an essay or story
14. _____ and cons
17. A part of speech that shows action or state-of-being

After You Read

Word Search

Find the following key words from the story. The words are written horizontally, vertically, diagonally and some are even backwards.

adjectives	graphic	paragraph	revising
brainstorming	narrative	persuasive	thesis
drafting	objective	prompts	verbs
essay	organizers	pros and cons	
expository	outline	reports	

g	j	w	e	s	s	a	y	u	o	s	r	g	s	p
k	y	l	h	t	k	w	i	e	b	w	r	e	e	x
w	s	p	t	r	l	d	m	r	e	a	v	r	p	b
e	r	e	q	o	e	b	e	y	p	i	s	r	y	f
v	e	v	l	p	d	v	r	h	t	u	o	m	e	b
i	z	i	g	e	g	a	i	c	a	m	j	n	o	y
t	i	t	t	r	j	c	e	s	p	d	i	h	g	r
c	n	a	h	b	e	j	i	t	r	l	l	p	n	o
e	a	r	e	j	d	v	s	a	t	n	g	a	i	t
j	g	r	s	a	e	o	f	u	p	q	g	r	s	i
b	r	a	i	n	s	t	o	r	m	i	n	g	i	s
o	o	n	s	r	i	u	q	u	o	h	h	a	v	o
s	i	w	r	n	c	r	s	t	w	f	k	r	e	p
u	e	x	g	j	q	k	h	j	p	k	c	a	r	x
r	m	s	n	o	c	d	n	a	s	o	r	p	l	e

NAME: _____

Comprehension Quiz

32

1. In complete sentences, describe how a paragraph and an essay are related.

7

_____

2. In complete sentences, describe the parts of an essay.

_____

3. List the five steps in the writing process.

a) _____

b) _____

c) _____

d) _____

e) _____

4. Circle the word True if the statement is true. Circle the word False if it's false.

a) A paragraph is a collection of sentences about the same topic.

   True   False

b) Brainstorming is part of the drafting step in writing.

   True   False

c) Prompts are suggested topics for essays.

   True   False

d) A sensory chart is a graphic organizer that lists all the steps in a process in the order they happened.

   True   False

e) A persuasive essay is one that describes something.

   True   False

f) A sequence chart lists the details of the sights, tastes, smells, touches, and sounds of a topic.

   True   False

g) The purpose of an informative essay is to show, tell, or review.

   True   False

7

SUBTOTAL: /14

 48

NAME: _____

After You Read

Comprehension Quiz

4. **Identify each essay type by placing an I before each informative prompt, a P before each persuasive prompt, an N before each narrative prompt, and a D before each descriptive prompt.**

- [ ] **a)** write about the insects in Australia
- [ ] **b)** write about the best birthday you ever had.
- [ ] **c)** write about why you believe there should be a three day school week.
- [ ] **d)** describe your favorite kind of ice cream
- [ ] **e)** should boys and girls go to separate schools
- [ ] **f)** What is your favorite time of year?
- [ ] **g)** If I Were an Astronaut
- [ ] **h)** Should your family move to a new city?
- [ ] **i)** The Causes of the Civil War
- [ ] **j)** The Story of Paul Bunyan and Babe the Blue Ox

5. **Circle the adjectives (describing words) in each sentence below:**

- **a)** Cass was wearing her ugly, green coat. (2)
- **b)** I saw a shiny penny in the grass. (1)
- **c)** That was the best cake I ever ate! (1)
- **d)** Seven aliens tiptoed from the spaceship. (1)
- **e)** Trevor read twenty-two books last summer. (1)
- **f)** That is the worst game I've ever played. (1)
- **g)** Marie is a sad girl. (1)
- **h)** I love to brush my beautiful red hair! (2)

SUBTOTAL: /18

© CLASSROOM COMPLETE PRESS

49

How to Write an Essay CC1102

![EZ✓]

1.
a) chronological outline
b) drafting
c) order of importance ladder
d) informal outline
e) rough draft
f) purpose

2.
accept any reasonable answer

15

1. Chronological Order Chart

2. Order of Importance

3. Informal Outline

13

1.
to tell a story

2.
persuasive

3.
to present information about the topic

4.
descriptive

5.
a) FALSE
b) TRUE
c) FALSE

12

1	D
2	K
3	G
4	B
5	I
6	C
7	J
8	H
9	A
10	E
11	F

10

1.
a) paragraph
b) essay
c) process
d) prewriting
e) proofreading
f) revising
g) drafting
h) publishing
i) prompts
j) purpose

9

1.
a) essay
b) five paragraphs
c) three
d) introduction
e) body
f) conclusion
g) five
h) prewriting
i) graphic organizers
j) drafting
k) revising
l) proofreading
m) publishing
n) purpose
o) accept any reasonable answer

7

25

1. accept any reasonable response

24

1. accept any reasonable response

2. a), c) and e)

22

1.
a) "be" verbs
b) narrative essay
c) sequence
d) mind movie
e) action verbs
f) sensory
g) powerful

2.
a) galloped
b) dodged, raced
c) crackled
d) marched, saluted
e) sings
f) twisted, turned
g) raced
h) buzzed, startled

21

1. accept any reasonable response

19

1.
1 F
2 D
3 A
4 E
5 G
6 B
7 C

2.
a) dark, stormy
b) two, four
c) shaggy, fluffy
d) red, black
e) ten, fifteen

18

1. b) and d)

2.
a) favorite
b) famous
c) excellent
d) loud
e) little

1. accept any reasonable answers

2.
a) describe something
b) subjective, objective
c) language
d) planning
e) mental picture
f) Spider

1.
a), b) and **d)**

2.
to cause other people to change their minds about an issue and to think like the writer thinks.

3.
A narrative essay tells a story while a persuasive essay tries to change someone's mind.

4.
for and against

5.
Accept any reasonable answer.

34

accept any reasonable answers

33

1.
a) informative essay
b) thesis statement
c) outline
d) sources

2.
accept any reasonable response

31

accept any reasonable response

30

1.
b), d) and **e)**

2.
accept any reasonable response

28

1.
a) story
b) memories or ideas
c) understand, details
d) unified, one
e) sequential or chronological

2.
accept any reasonable response

27

1.
a) It's
b) it's
c) It's
d) they're, their
e) there
f) they're

2.
a) Alex and Sam read How to eat Fried Worms by Thomas Rockwell.
b) I met Kim while I was staying at the Grand Hotel in Michigan.
c) Dr. Jones said, "You'll be fine if you and Joey don't get into any more fights!"
d) We bought milk, eggs, bacon, and bread at the store.
e) Sam, can you help me with this package?
f) Kwan lives in Saratoga, New York.
g) My grandmother's favorite song is "Rock Around the Clock".

3.
a) Who's
b) couldn't, children's
c) woman's
d) won't
e) work
f) learn
g) teach

(42)

1. revising

2. looking for any mistakes that have been made

3. rest, read, make changes

4. Resting a bit before revising provides "fresh eyes" to look for changes to be made and any mistakes that need to be changed.

5. The Christmas Surprise

Last Christmas was the best holiday that I ever had! All of my family was together in one place for the first time in years. Dad was working on a present for Mom and me in the garage. My brother, Jim, was home on leave from the Army. Grandpa and Grandma were coming to see us on Christmas day. It doesn't matter how many presents you get, love is the most special present of all. Having everyone here in one house made this the best holiday ever!

accept any reasonable responses

(40)

(39)

1.
1 E
2 F
3 A
4 C
5 D
6 B

2. Accept any reasonable answer.

(37)

1. Accept any reasonable answer.

2.
a) FALSE
b) TRUE
c) FALSE
d) TRUE
e) FALSE

(36)

Word Search Answers

Across
5. informative
6. biography
7. prewriting
8. adjectives
10. brainstorming
13. graphic
15. revision
16. paragraph
18. outline
19. objective

Down
1. expository
2. proofreading
3. publishing
4. reports
9. drafting
11. narrative
12. prompt
14. pros
17. verb

1.
A paragraph is a collection of sentences related to the same topic. An essay is a collection of paragraphs related to the same topic.

2.
The first paragraph is the introduction. The second, third, and fourth paragraphs are the body of the essay.

The fifth paragraph is the conclusion.

3.
a) prewriting
b) drafting
c) revising
d) proofreading
e) publishing

4.
a) TRUE
b) FALSE
c) TRUE
d) FALSE
e) FALSE
f) FALSE
g) TRUE

4.
a) I
b) N
c) P
d) D
e) P
f) D
g) N
h) P
i) I
j) N

5.
a) ugly, green
b) shiny
c) best
d) seven
e) twenty-two
f) worst
g) sad
h) beautiful, red

Concept Map

● ● ● ● ● ● ● ● ● ● ● ● ● ● ●

Reason 1

Reason 2

My Opinion:

Reason 3

Reason 4

Expository Pillar-Prewriting Framework

● ● ● ● ● ● ● ● ● ● ● ● ●

This graphic organizer will enable students to "build" their informative essay and transfer it into sentences and paragraphs in the drafting stage.

Introduction (lead/thesis statement):

Main Idea #1:

Details:	

Main Idea #2:

Details:	

Main Idea #3:

Details:	

Conclusion:

Descriptive Essay Graphic Organizer

This graphic organizer will be a great help when you plan a descriptive essay. Remember that a descriptive essay's purpose is simply to **describe** something or someone.

Introduction Paragraph

Where I am describing?	
How I will organize this essay? (spatial, time and importance order)	

Body Paragraph 1

Sensory Detail	*Specific Example*
Figure of Speech (Simile Metaphor or Personification)	*Specific Example*

Body Paragraph 2

Sensory Detail	*Specific Example*
Sensory Detail	*Specific Example*

Body Paragraph 3

Sensory Detail	*Specific Example*
Sensory Detail	*Specific Example*

Conclusion

Why is this place important to you?	

Gathering Grid

A gathering grid can help you organize information for a research report.
- Write your questions in the left hand column
- Write the title of your sources at the top of each column
- Write answers you find and note where you found them

Topic	Source 1	Source 2	Source 3
Question 1			
Question 2			
Question 3			

Persuasive Essay Organizer

INTRODUCTION

Main Idea Topic Sentence:_____

Supporting Reasons: Body 1_____

Body 2 _____

Body 3 _____

Conclusion sentence:_____

BODY #1

Reason #1 _____

Detail/Example 1 _____

Detail/Example 2 _____

Detail/Example 3 _____

Conclusion sentence:_____

BODY #2

Reason #1 _____

Detail/Example 1 _____

Detail/Example 2 _____

Detail/Example 3 _____

Conclusion sentence:_____

BODY #3

Reason #1 _____

Detail/Example 1 _____

Detail/Example 2 _____

Detail/Example 3 _____

Conclusion sentence:_____

CONCLUSION

Restate Main Idea: _____

Restate Supporting Reasons: Reason 1 _____

Reason 2_____

Reason 3_____

Recommendations and/or Predictions: _____

Story Map

● ● ● ● ● ● ● ● ● ● ● ● ● ● ●

This story map is helpful when students plan to write a fictional narrative essay. By listing all the areas to be considered before the actual writing begins, this map is a very useful planning tool. A story map can help you plot out just what happens in a story.

- Fill in each part of the story map.
- Use the story map to guide your writing.

Title

Main Characters

Other Characters

Conflict

Setting

Rising Action #1

Rising Action #2

Rising Action #3

Climax

Resolution